KU-172-339

NEW TESTAMENT

JOHN

Believe and have life

Matt Malcolm

youthworks

First published March 2005
Revised edition published January 2012

Anglican Youthworks
PO Box A287,
Sydney South NSW 1235

Ph: 612 8268 3344
Fax: 612 8268 3357
www.cepstore.com.au

Copyright Youthworks Press © Matt Malcolm 2011
This book is copyright. Apart from fair dealing for the purposes of private
study, research, criticism or review, as permitted under the Copyright
Act 1968, no part may be reproduced by any process without the written
permission of the Publisher.

Scriptures taken from The Holy Bible, New International Version® NIV®.
Copyright© 1973, 1978, 1984 by International Bible Society. Used by
permission. All rights reserved worldwide.

National Library of Australia
ISBN 978-1-922000-20-0

Author – Matt Malcolm
Editor, First edition – Julie Moser
Managing Editor, Revised edition – Julie Firmstone
Theological Editor – Marshall Ballantine-Jones
Typesetting and design – Rebecca Jee

INTRODUCING JOHN

Welcome to John's account of Jesus' life, death and resurrection (also known as John's Gospel). Over the next few weeks these studies will help you dig into the highlights of John's Gospel on the theme of believing.

WHY WAS JOHN'S GOSPEL WRITTEN?

Almost at the end of the book, John gave us the reason why he wrote this account of Jesus.

> Jesus performed many other signs in the presence of his disciples, which are not recorded in this book. But these are written that you may believe that Jesus is the Messiah, the Son of God, and that by believing you may have life in his name.
>
> John 20:30–31

All that John had recorded in his gospel (message) contributed to his purpose for writing—to convince his readers about Jesus and their need to respond to him, by believing in order to have real life that lasts forever.

WHO IS JOHN?

The writer of John's Gospel was John the apostle, one of the twelve disciples of Jesus. John and his brother James, along with Peter and Andrew (all fishing partners), were called to follow Jesus together (see Mark 1:16–20). John was known as the 'the disciple whom Jesus loved' (John 13:23; 19:26–27) and was the only disciple recorded to have witnessed Jesus' crucifixion, along with some women (John 19:25–27). John was one of the early church leaders and recognised by Paul as a 'pillar of the church' (Galatians 2:9).

SOME THEMES WE'LL BE LOOKING AT

John's Gospel deals with many themes including:

- believing in Jesus
- reasons for believing
- being born again
- unbelief
- real life
- doubt.

John was keen to show us that believing in Jesus is awesome. These studies will help us to see what it means to believe—in a world that often doesn't—and to see the great benefits that Christians receive. Hopefully over the next few weeks you'll see how great it is to believe in Jesus, too.

Believe and have life!

Matt Malcolm

FOR GOD SO LOVED THE
WORLD THAT HE GAVE HIS
ONE AND ONLY SON, THAT
WHOEVER BELIEVES IN HIM
SHALL NOT PERISH BUT
HAVE ETERNAL LIFE.

JOHN 3:16

1 INTRODUCING JESUS
JOHN 1:1–18

SHARE

What are some different ways that we communicate with each other?

If you had to make yourself known to someone in a different country, how would you do it?

THE WORD OF GOD

Read John 1:1–8

Have a look at the beginnings of Matthew (1:1 and 1:17), Mark (1:1–4 and 1:7) and Luke (1:1–4). **How was John's beginning different?**

Write out a reference for the person introduced by John in verses 1–4:

What is surprising about this person? Who was it?

Date of birth:

Name:

Address:

Previous experience:

Strengths:

Other ...

PEOPLE RESPOND TO THE WORD

Identify the different people (or groups of people) in the passage and how they responded to Jesus.

PERSON (OR GROUP)	RESPONSE TO JESUS

How do we become children of God?
(verses 12–13)

Make a list of the benefits of being a child of God.

What do you think it means to believe in Jesus?

GOD BECOMES HUMAN

Looking at John 1:14 and 18 draw (or write) in the space below what these verses tell us about how God made himself known to us.

YOU AND JESUS

Today's passage is all about Jesus. He is God in human form and he makes it possible for us to become children of God. **Read the statements below and place a tick next to the statement that best describes your relationship to Jesus and then discuss your answers:**

_____✓ I believe in Jesus. I trust him with my life.

_____✓ I'm not sure where I stand with Jesus.

_____ My life is too busy right now for Jesus.

_____ I'd like to get to know more about believing in Jesus.

_____ My life is moving in a direction away from Jesus.

What stops people from believing in Jesus? (Believing in Jesus = trusting Jesus)

PRAY

Thank God for making himself known to us in Jesus.

Ask him to help us trust Jesus and to live as his children.

MEMORY VERSE

But these are written that you might believe that Jesus is the Christ, the Son of God, and that by believing you might have life in his name.

John 20:31

2 REASONS TO BELIEVE IN JESUS
JOHN 2:1–25

SHARE

Name some people you trust.

Why do you trust them?

Why do people trust each other?

WATER INTO WINE

Read John 2:1–11

Imagine you are a reporter for the Cana local newspaper doing a story on this event.
What would be the headline for your story?

The Cana Herald

As the reporter, write down a statement from the following people about what they experienced at the wedding:

Jesus' mother (verses 1–5)

The servants (verses 5–10)

The master of the banquet (verses 9–10)

Verse 11 tells us that this was a sign that revealed Jesus' glory. **What information about Jesus did this 'sign' give to those at the wedding?**

What did the disciples do as a result of this 'sign'?

JESUS GOES TO THE TEMPLE

Read John 2:12–25

The temple symbolised the presence of God with his people. People were not able to approach God because of their sin; however they could sacrifice an animal as payment for their sin in the temple. For this reason people would sell animals for people to sacrifice—sometimes at a very high price!

What did Jesus find in the temple courts? (verse 14)

What did he do? (verses 15–16)

Why do you think he was angry? (verse 16)

What claim did Jesus make in verse 19 and what was he talking about? (verses 21–22)

What did the disciples believe about Jesus' claim and when did they believe it? (verse 22)

REASONS FOR TRUSTING IN JESUS

What are some reasons people give for not trusting Jesus?

List some reasons that the book of John has given us so far for why Jesus can be trusted and then discuss your answers.

Give the reasons why you trust (believe) in Jesus OR the reasons why you do not yet trust (believe) in him.

PRAY

Thank God that Jesus has shown himself to be trustworthy.

Ask God to help you keep on trusting Jesus in your life.

MEMORY VERSE

But these are written that you might believe that Jesus is the Christ, the Son of God, and that by believing you might have life in his name.

John 20:31

3 BELIEVING AND BEING BORN AGAIN
JOHN 3:1-21

SHARE

Circle the words in the list below that describe a great family:

PROVIDES SECURITY

CLOSE

FUN

BUSY

TALKS ABOUT THINGS

FRIENDSHIP

SISTERS / BROTHERS

KIND

LOVING

OTHER:

_____

HOLIDAYS TOGETHER

Why do the things you have chosen from the list above make a family great?

What did you have to do to become a member of your family?

BEING BORN AGAIN

Read John 3:1–15

What sort of person was Nicodemus? (verse 1)

What sort of person did he think Jesus was? (verse 2)

What instruction did Jesus give Nicodemus? (verses 3 and 5–8)

What did Nicodemus think Jesus meant when he said that a person must be 'born again'? (verse 4)

Look at John 1:12–13. What does it mean to be 'born again'?

In verses 13–15 Jesus used a story from the Old Testament to help Nicodemus understand him.

Read Numbers 21:4–9

What happened when the people looked at the bronze snake that Moses lifted up?

Look again at John 3:13–15 and work out what Jesus was saying about himself (the Son of Man).

Jesus' death brings eternal life to all who look to him and believe. **Look at the verses below and write down what they tell us about Jesus' death:**

Mark 10:45

Romans 5:8–10

Hebrews 9:15

BELIEVING AND BEING BORN AGAIN

Being born again is being born new into God's family. John was eager to show us that there is only one way that this can happen.

Read John 3:16–21

WHAT DO VERSES 16-21 TELL US ABOUT:

God	
Jesus	
Believers	
Unbelievers	

On the basis of this passage how do I become a member of God's family?

Not everyone is born into God's family because not everyone believes in Jesus. **Discuss some things we can do to help others believe in Jesus.**

What can you do this week to encourage a non-Christian friend to consider believing in Jesus?

PRAY

Thank God for providing a way to be born into his family.

Pray for friends/family whom you would like to see come to believe in Jesus and become a member of God's family.

MEMORY VERSE

But these are written that you might believe that Jesus is the Christ, the Son of God, and that by believing you might have life in his name.

John 20:31

FURTHER READING

Try to read John chapters 4 and 5 in the week to come.

4 BELIEVING AND UNBELIEF
JOHN 6:1–15, 25–35, 53–70

SHARE

Place a tick alongside the activities listed that you really like doing:

___ Playing a team sport   ___ Learning to dance

___ Learning an instrument   ___ Drama

___ Playing computers   ___ Woodwork

___ Maths   ___ Gymnastics

___ Cooking   ___ Learning another language

___ Going to youth group   ___ Other: _____

What are some things you have started but never continued?

JESUS FEEDS 5000

Read John 6:1–15

What was the problem in this story? (verses 5–7)

How did Jesus deal with the problem? (verses 10–11)

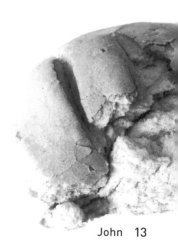

What did the people think about Jesus after he had fed them? (verses 14–15)

What does this story teach us about Jesus?

THE BREAD OF LIFE

Read John 6:25–35

Compare what the people following Jesus wanted from him and what Jesus wanted for the people and write your answers in the spaces below:

WHAT DID THE PEOPLE WANT FROM JESUS?	WHAT DID JESUS WANT FOR THE PEOPLE?
Verses 25–26	Verse 27
Verses 30–31	Verses 32–35

The reason the crowd followed Jesus was to be physically satisfied. However, Jesus wanted them to be spiritually satisfied. People call themselves Christians (believers in Jesus) for different reasons. **Circle the reasons below that you think are wrong reasons to say you are a Christian and then discuss your answers:**

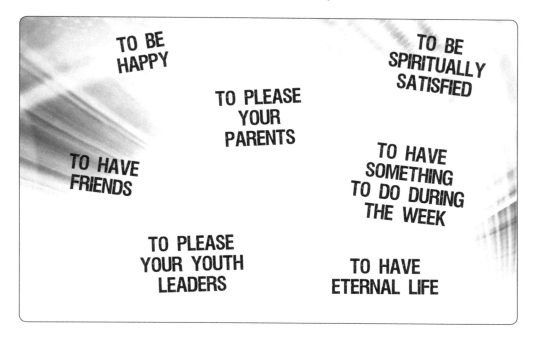

TO BE HAPPY

TO PLEASE YOUR PARENTS

TO BE SPIRITUALLY SATISFIED

TO HAVE FRIENDS

TO HAVE SOMETHING TO DO DURING THE WEEK

TO PLEASE YOUR YOUTH LEADERS

TO HAVE ETERNAL LIFE

BELIEVING AND UNBELIEF

Read John 6:53–70

Jesus had many people following him for different reasons. Jesus taught some things that were hard for the crowd to accept (to eat his flesh and drink his blood which means to believe in his death for you—verse 53).

What did some of Jesus' disciples do as a result of his hard teaching? (verse 66)

Why did the twelve disciples stand firm in their belief in Jesus? (verses 68–69)

STICKING WITH THE CHRISTIAN FAITH

When times get hard our belief in Jesus can be tested. Those who do not have a genuine faith in Jesus often fall away. **Discuss what things cause people to stop following Jesus.**

What can help us stand firm in our faith in Jesus?

Spend some time this week reflecting on whether you are following Jesus for the right reasons.

PRAY

Ask God to help you stick with the Christian faith. Pray for anyone you know who may be struggling.

MEMORY VERSE

But these are written that you might believe that Jesus is the Christ, the Son of God, and that by believing you might have life in his name.

John 20:31

FURTHER READING

Try to read John chapters 8–10 in the week to come.

SHARE

Circle three things from the list below that best describe your life, and then discuss your answers:

BORING

SERIOUS

FUN

EASY

BUSY

JOYFUL

TIRING

EXCITING

FAITHFUL
CHRISTIAN

HARD

OTHER:

_____

DEPRESSING

CHAOTIC

Describe the perfect life in one sentence.

THE DEATH OF LAZARUS

Read John 11:1–6

List each of the people in this story and what we're told about them.

NAME	INFORMATION ABOUT THEM

What two reasons did Jesus give for the events that were about to happen regarding the death of Lazarus?

Verse 4

Verses 14–15

LIFE THROUGH JESUS

Read John 11:17–37

When Jesus arrived in Bethany, Lazarus had been dead for four days (verse 17).
Give a summary of the conversation that took place between Martha and Jesus in verses 21–27.

What did Martha believe about Jesus?

Jesus made an amazing claim in verses 25–26. **Explain in your own words what you think he meant.**

What is so amazing about this claim?

Read John 11:38–45

How does this part of the story back up Jesus' claim in verses 25–26?

BELIEVING AND LIFE

If you were to die tomorrow, how sure are you that you will 'live even though you die'? **Place a cross on the scale below to indicate how sure you are, then discuss your answers:**

0%   **50%**   **100%**

Jesus claimed that he is the resurrection and the life. **Look at the following verses and see what else John has told us about Jesus and life:**

John 3:36

John 5:24–27

John 14:6

How can you be 100% sure that you would have eternal life if you were to die tomorrow?

How will knowing that you will live even after you die affect the way you live now? (Give some examples of how your life will be different if you believe this.)

PRAY

Thank God for giving us life through Jesus.

Ask him to help you live like Jesus wants you to.

MEMORY VERSE

But these are written that you might believe that Jesus is the Christ, the Son of God, and that by believing you might have life in his name.

John 20:31

FURTHER READING

Try to read John chapters 12–18 in the week to come—this is a long section but full of great stuff!

6 BELIEVING AND THE DEATH OF JESUS
JOHN 19:16–37

SHARE

If you were asked to give a list of your top five 'good things', what would they be?

1. _____

2. _____

3. _____

4. _____

5. _____

Sometimes good things come as a result of bad events. **Can you think of any times when good things came from something bad?** (For example, people unite together when there is a tragedy amongst them.)

THE CRUCIFIXION OF JESUS

Read John 19:16–37

The writers of the Old Testament predicted the life and death of Jesus. **Look up these Old Testament passages and find which part of the death of Jesus each passage predicted:**

OLD TESTAMENT PASSAGE	PART OF JESUS' DEATH IT PREDICTED
Psalm 22:18	
Psalm 69:21	
Psalm 34:20	
Zechariah 12:10	

The fact that Jesus' death was predicted hundreds of years beforehand in the Old Testament shows us that God had planned this from the beginning. God planned good things to come out of this one bad event.

What do we learn from John about these good things? Have a look at:

John 1:29 (see also 1 Peter 3:18–21. **How does a lamb take away sin?)**

John 10:11

John 12:23–24

What did John want us to believe about the account of Jesus' death as told in the book of John? (See John 19:35.)

THE BENEFITS OF JESUS' DEATH

What did Jesus' death do for us who believe in him? Have a look at the following passages and write down what each one says about Jesus' death and what it did for us:

2 Corinthians 5:21

Galatians 4:4–5

Colossians 1:21–22

1 John 4:9–10

Christians receive many 'good things' because of Christ's death. **What would you say is the best thing about being a Christian? Give reasons for your answer.**

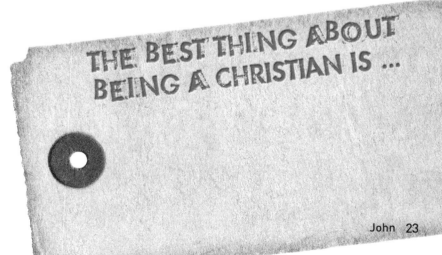

THE BEST THING ABOUT BEING A CHRISTIAN IS ...

PRAY

Thank God that he always planned to send Jesus for us.

Thank him for sending Jesus to die in our place.

MEMORY VERSE

But these are written that you might believe that Jesus is the Christ, the Son of God, and that by believing you might have life in his name.

John 20:31

7 BELIEVING, DOUBT AND THE RESURRECTION
JOHN 20:24–31

SHARE

Circle the things you doubt will happen in your lifetime:

FLUORESCENT PINK
CLOTHES WILL
MAKE A COMEBACK

HUMANS WILL
LIVE ON MARS

WORLD
PEACE

JESUS WILL
RETURN

YOU WILL GO
OVERSEAS

THE LEANING
TOWER OF PISA
WILL FALL OVER

GLOBAL WARMING
WILL RESULT IN
THE FLOODING OF
THE EARTH

What are some things you have no doubt about?

JESUS AND THOMAS

Read John 20:24–31

Jesus died on the cross, was buried in a tomb and came back from the dead. He appeared to Mary and some of his disciples. However, one of the disciples (Thomas) was not with them when they first saw the resurrected Jesus. **What did Thomas say must happen before he would believe?** (verse 25)

Jesus appeared again to the disciples—including Thomas—a week later (verses 26–29). **List the interaction between Jesus and Thomas. (Write in your own words what each of them said.)**

Jesus
(verses 26–27)

Thomas
(verse 28)

Jesus
(verse 29)

In verse 29, Jesus spoke of those who had seen him and those who hadn't seen him. Thomas was amongst those who had seen Jesus face to face and believed. **Who were the people who believed without having seen Jesus face to face?**

How can someone believe in Jesus if they haven't seen him face to face?
(verses 30–31)

Verse 31 is the key to understanding the book of John. **What are the two reasons this book has been written?**

1.

2.

BELIEVING AND DOUBT

What can cause you to sometimes doubt the Christian faith?

List three things that can help you to continue believing in Jesus through times of doubt:

1.

2.

3.

JOHN'S ACCOUNT OF JESUS

What are some of your favourite parts of the book of John?

What have you learned from John about believing in Jesus?

What is one area in your life you have been challenged to change as a result of studying the book of John?

PRAY

Thank God for the things you have learned.

Ask God to help you continue to trust Jesus and live for him.

MEMORY VERSE

Who can recite the memory verse? Spend some time now reciting the memory verse until everyone has had a go.

FURTHER READING

Read through the whole book of John. Note how often he uses the word 'believe'.